boyzone...by re

boyzone...by re

this publication is not authorised for sale in
the united states of america and / or canada

wise publications

london / new york / sydney / paris / copenhagen / madrid

exclusive distributors: **music sales limited**, 8/9 frith street, london w1v 5tz, england. **music sales pty limited**, 120 rothschild avenue, rosebery, nsw 2018, australia. order no.am959398. isbn 0-7119-7442-X. this book © copyright 1999 by **wise publications**. www.internetmusicshop.com

your guarantee of quality: as publishers, we strive to produce every book to the highest commercial standards. the music has been freshly engraved and the book has been carefully designed to minimise awkward page turns and to make playing from it a real pleasure. particular care has been given to specifying acid-free, neutral-sized paper made from pulps which have not been elemental chlorine bleached. this pulp is from farmed sustainable forests and was produced with special regard for the environment. throughout, the printing and binding have been planned to ensure a sturdy, attractive publication which should give years of enjoyment. if your copy fails to meet our high standards, please inform us and we will gladly replace it.

music sales' complete catalogue describes thousands of titles and is available in full colour sections by subject, direct from **music sales limited**. please state your areas of interest and send a cheque / postal order for £1.50 for postage to: **music sales limited**, newmarket road, bury st. edmunds, suffolk ip33 3yb.

i love the way you love me 04

no matter what 09

all that i need 18

baby can i hold you? 14

picture of you 23

isn't it a wonder? 28

a different beat 33

words 38

father and son 42

so good 47

coming home now 52

key to my life 58

love me for a reason 63

when the going gets tough 68

you needed me 76

when you say nothing at all 80

all the time in the world 86

i'll never not need you 91

i love the way you love me

1. I like the feel—— of your name on my lips and I like the sound—— of your sweet

Verse 3:
And I like the sound of old R and B
You roll your eyes when I'm slightly off key
And I like the innocent way that you cry
From sappy old movies you've seen thousands of times.

But I love *etc.*

no matter what

music by andrew lloyd webber. lyrics by jim steinman. © copyright 1998 the really useful group limited, 22 tower street, london wc2 (50%) & lost boys music/polygram music publishing limited, 47 british grove, london w4 (50%). all rights reserved. international copyright secured.

Unhurried

No mat-ter what they tell us, no mat-ter what they do,
If on-ly tears were laugh-ter, if on-ly night was day,

no mat-ter what they teach us, what we be-lieve is true.
if on-ly prayers were an-swered then we would hear God say.

No mat - ter what they call us,   how - ev - er they at -
No mat - ter what they tell you,   no mat - ter what they

- tack,   no mat - ter where they take us,
do,   no mat - ter what they teach you,

we'll find our own way back.   I can't de - ny what I
what you be - lieve is true.   And I will keep you safe

be - lieve,   I can't be what I'm not.
and strong   and shel - tered from the storm.

I know our love's for - ev - er,
No mat - ter where it's bar - ren

I know no mat - ter what.—
our dream is be - ing born.—

baby can i hold you?

words & music by tracy chapman.

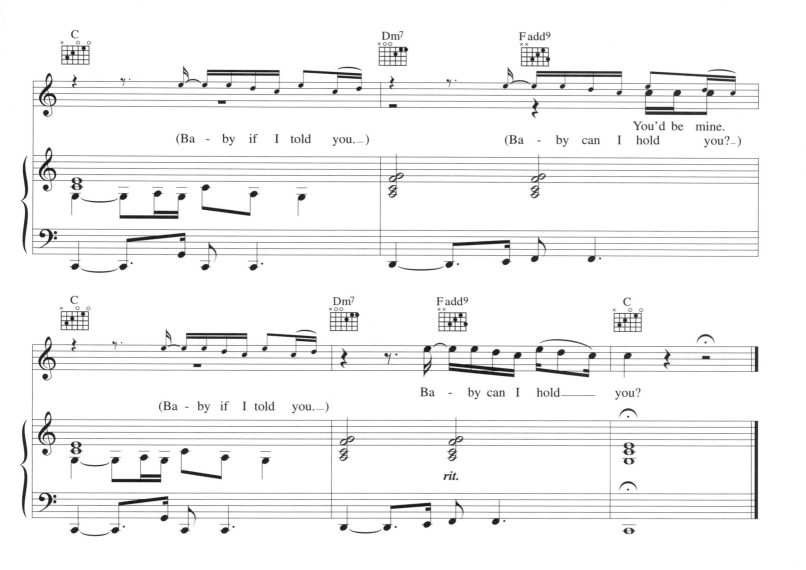

Verse 2:
Forgive me is all that you can't say
Years gone by and still
Words don't come easily
Like forgive me, forgive me.

Verse 3:
I love you is all that you can't say
Years gone by and still
Words don't come easily
Like I love you, I love you.

all that i need

words & music by evan rogers & carl sturken. © copyright 1995 bayjun beat music/music corporation of america, usa. mca music limited, 77 fulham palace road, london w6.

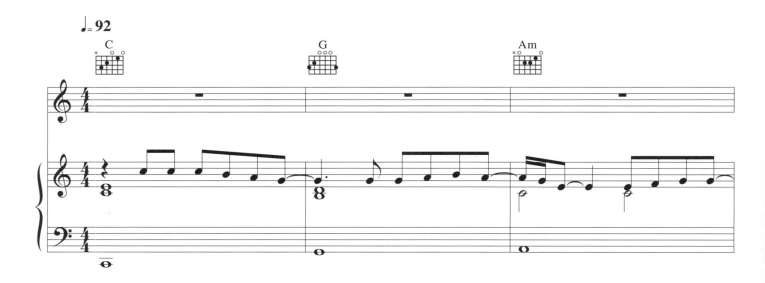

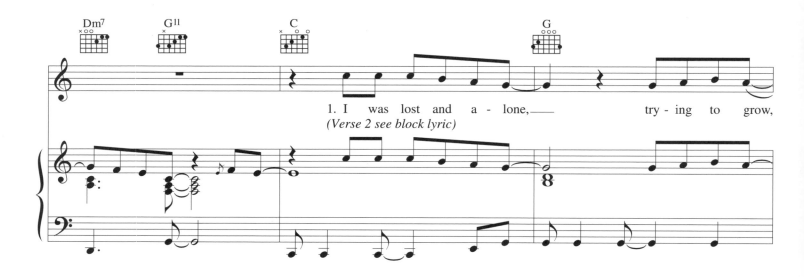

1. I was lost and a - lone,____ try - ing to grow,
(Verse 2 see block lyric)

____ mak - ing my way____ down that long____ wind - ing road.____ Had no rea - son or rhyme

You're the air that I breathe__ girl, you're all that I need.__

__ And I wan-na thank__ you la-dy.__ You're the words that I read,__

__ you're the light that I see,__ and your love is all__ that I need.__

Verse 2:

I was searching in vain, playing your game
Had no-one else but myself left to blame
You came into my world, no diamonds or pearls
Could ever replace what you gave to me girl
Just like a castle of sand
Girl I almost let love
Slip right out of my hand
And just like a flower needs rain
I will stand by your side
Through the joy and the pain.

You're the air that I breathe *etc.*

picture of you

it, I did-n't want to know.

I let you in and you
(Verse 2 see block lyric)

let me down. You messed me up and you turned

my life a - round. Left me feel-ing I had no-where to go, I was a - lone,

how was I to know that?

the friend— that was there— all a - long?—

Verse 2:
Do you believe that after all that we've been through
I'd be able to put my trust in you?
Goes to show you can forgive and forget
Looking back I have no regrets, cos

You were with me there *etc.*

isn't it a wonder?

words & music by martin brannigan, ronan keating & ray hedges. © copyright 1996 polygram music publishing limited, 47 british grove, london w4 (33.34%), island music limited, 47 british grove, london w4 (33.33%) & 19 music / bmg music publishing limited, 69-79 fulham palace road, london w6 (33.33%). this arrangement © copyright 1999 bmg music publishing limited for their share of interest. all rights reserved. international copyright secured.

1. It's a sign of the times girl, sad songs on the ra - di - o.____
(Verse 2 see block lyric)

It's a sign of the times girl, as the leaves be - gin to go.____ But all these signs now,

Verse 2:

It's the way of the world
When wrong takes hold of right.
It's the way of the world
In which we've all lost sight.
But isn't this world too simple to be true,
Holding on to memories of you.

a different beat

words & music by martin brannigan, stephen gately, ronan keating, shane lynch, ray hedges & keith duffy.

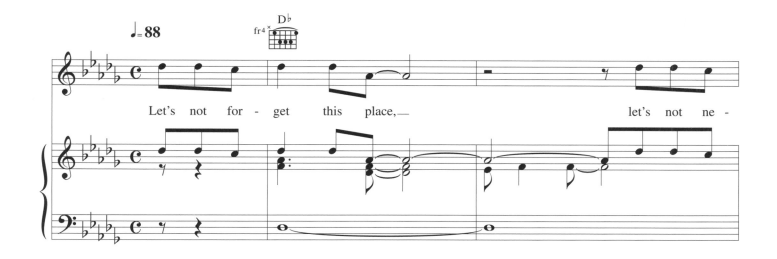

Let's not for - get this place, ___ let's not ne -

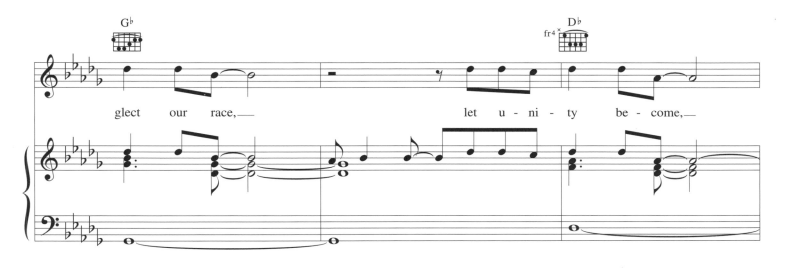

glect our race, ___ let u - ni - ty be - come, ___

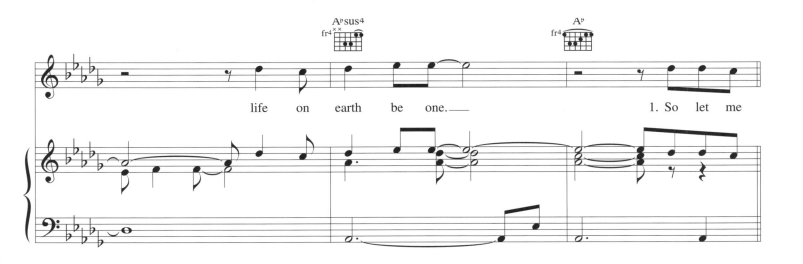

life on earth be one. ___ 1. So let me

take your hand,— we are but grains of sand,— born through the
(Verse 2 see block lyric)

winds of time,— giv-en a spe-cial sign.— So

let's take a stand and look a-round us now,— peo-ple.———— So

let's take a stand and look a-round us now,— peo-ple.———— Ee-

yea oh,___ ee - yea oh,___ ee - yea oh,___ by - yah.__

(To a dif - fer - ent beat.)

Ee - yea oh,___ ee - yea oh,___ ee -

yea oh,___ by - yah._____ 2. Hu - man - i -

I've seen the rain fall in Af - ri - ca,_____ I've touched the snows of A -

Verse 2:
Humanity has lost face,
Let's understand its grace,
Each day, one at a time,
Each life, including mine.

Let's take a stand and look around us now,
People,
So let's take a stand and look around us now,
People, oh people, oh people.

words

words & music by barry gibb, robin gibb & maurice gibb.

Moderately slow

Smile an ev - er - last - ing smile; a smile could bring you near to me.

Don't ev - er let me find you

Talk in ev-er-last-ing words and ded-i-cate them all to me.

And I will give you all my life, I'm here if you should

call to me. You think that I don't e-ven

mean a sin-gle word I say. It's on-ly

father and son

words & music by cat stevens.

(Verse 2 see block lyric)

1. It's not time to make a change; just re-lax, take it ea - sy. You're still young, that's your fault; there's so much you have to know. Find a girl,

set - tle down;—— if you want,—— you—— can mar - ry. Look at me:——

1. I am old—— but I'm hap - py.—— 2. I was

2. —— be here—— to - mor - row,—— but your dreams may not.

How can I—— try to ex - plain?—— When I do——

(Verse 4 see block lyric)

Verse 2:

I was once like you are now;
And I know that it's not easy
To be calm when you've found something going on.
But take your time, think a lot;
Think of everything you've got.
For you will still be here tomorrow,
But your dreams may not.

Verse 4:

All the times that I've cried,
Keeping all the things I knew inside;
And it's hard, but it's harder to ignore it.
If they were right I'd agree,
But it's them they know, not me;
Now there's a way, and I know
That I have to go away.
I know I have to go.

so good

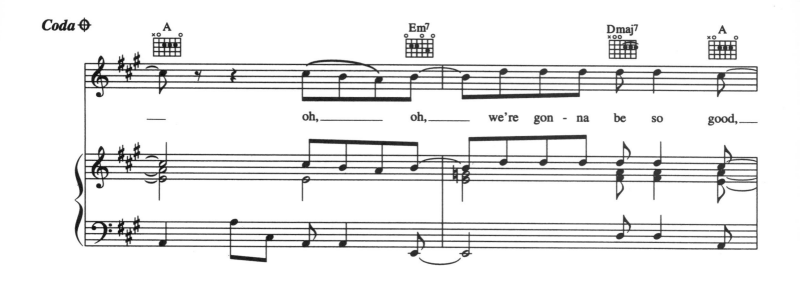

Coda ⊕

oh,_____ oh,_____ we're gon - na be so good,_____

like I knew we would,_____ you know we're good._____

Verse 2:
No matter the cost
When we're out on the town getting lazy
I'll show you who's boss
We're just gonna take it all the way
No matter what they say now.

coming home now

words & music by martin brannigan, stephen gately, ronan keating, michael graham, shane lynch, keith duffy & ray hedges.

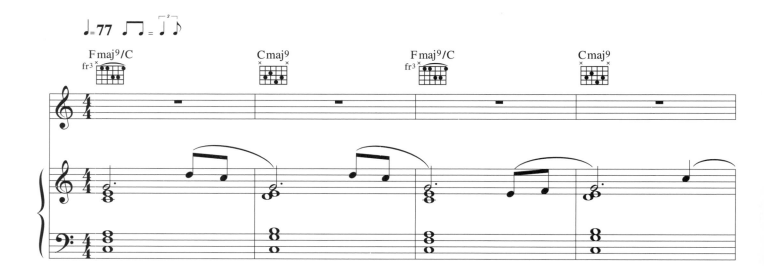

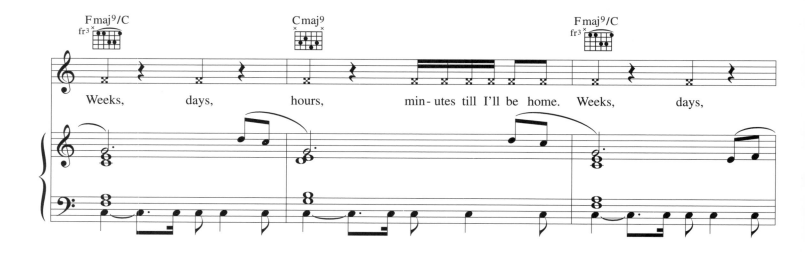

Weeks, days, hours, min- utes till I'll be home. Weeks, days,

hours, min- utes till I'll be home. Da da da da da da. Da da da da da da.

fine.   And there's a pic-ture, girl,_____ that hangs in-side my mind,_____ and there's a

let - ter, girl,_____ say I'm do-ing fine.   And I'm com-ing home_____

_____ now,_____ it's been so long_____ now._____ Gon - na get there some-

- how,_____ pray-ing you'll be there.   Com-ing home_____

54

key to my life

words & music by martin brannigan, stephen gately, ronan keating, michael graham & ray hedges. © copyright 1995 polygram music publishing limited, 47 british grove, london w4 (25%), island music limited, 47 british grove, london w4 (50%) & 19 music/bmg music publishing limited, bedford house, 69-79 fulham high street, london sw6 (25%). this arrangement © copyright 1999 bmg music publishing limited for their share of interest. all rights reserved. international copyright secured.

locked up in-side,___ but you came a-long___ and cap-tured my heart___ girl,

To Coda ⊕ | **1.**

you're the key___ to my life.

2.

life. Girl you know___ that I feel for you, there ain't no-thing that I would-n't do,

stop the thun-der and the pour-ing rain, you're the one___ that's gon-na stop the pain.

Verse 2:
Year after year was blaming myself
For what I'd done just thought of myself
I know that you'll understand this was all my fault
Don't go away.

love me for a reason

words & music by john bristol, wade brown jr. & david jones.

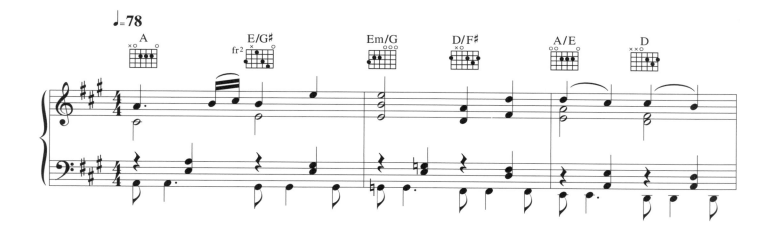

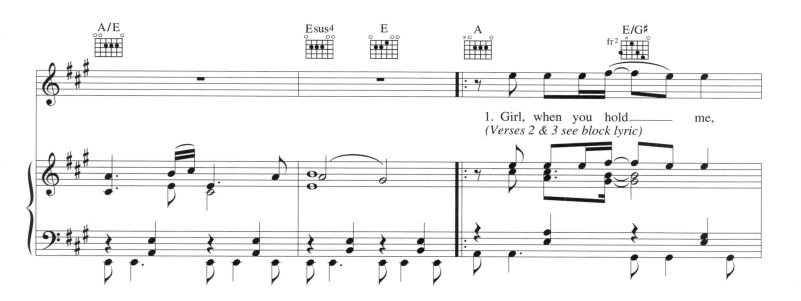

1. Girl, when you hold_____ me,
(Verses 2 & 3 see block lyric)

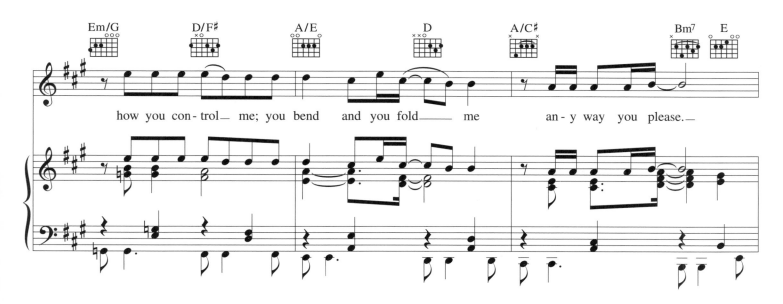

how you con-trol__ me; you bend and you fold____ me an-y way you please.__

let the rea - son be love.

D.%. al Coda

⊕ *Coda*

Don't love me for fun,— girl, let me be— the one, girl, love me for a rea - son,

let the rea - son be love. Don't love me for fun,— girl, let me be— the one, girl;

love me for a rea - son, let the rea - son be love. Don't love me for fun,— girl,

let me be— the one, girl, love me for a rea - son, let the rea - son be love.

Verse 2:
Kisses and caresses are only minor tests, babe,
Of love needs and stresses between a woman and a man.
So if love everlasting isn't what you're asking,
I'll have to pass, girl; I'm proud to take a stand.
I can't continue guessing, because it's only messing
With my pride and my mind.
So write down this time to time:

To Chorus

Verse 3:
I'm just a little old-fashioned,
It takes more than a physical attraction.
My initial reaction is "Honey, give me love;
Not a facsimile of."

To Chorus

when the going gets tough

words & music by wayne brathwaite, barry eastmond, robert john 'mutt' lange & billy ocean. © copyright 1985
zomba enterprises incorporated, aqua music limited & out of pocket productions limited, usa. all rights controlled by zomba music
publishers limited, 165-167 high road, london nw10. all rights reserved. international copyright secured.

(Verse 3 see block lyric)

get my - self 'cross the riv - er, that's the price____ I'm will-ing to pay.

____ I'm gon-na make you stand and de - liv - er, you give me

love in the old - fa-shioned way.____ Oh.____ (Dar - ling____) I'll climb

____ a - ny moun - tain. (Darl - ing____) I'll do____ a - ny - thing.____ Ooh____

(ooh,—) can I touch you (can I touch you) And do the things that lov-ers do?—

Ooh,— (ooh,—) wan-na hold— you. (Wan-na hold you) I

got-ta get it through to you.— Oh,— cos when the go-ing gets tough— (the

When the go - ing gets rough— oh,— (the tough get rough) Hey—

tough get go-ing)

(Dar - ling——) I'll climb—— a - ny moun - tain. (Dar - ling——) I'd swim

——— ev - 'ry sea.——— (Dar - ling——) I'd reach—— for - eign heav - ens

(Dar - - - ling———) with you——— lov - ing me.

Ooh——————— (ooh———————) ooh.——— Can I

Drums

touch___ you?___ (Can I touch you?) And do the things that lov - ers do.___

(Can I touch you?) Ooh___ (ooh___) wan-na hold___ you. (Wan-na hold you) I

got - ta get it through to you.___ Oh,___ cos when the

go-ing gets tough,___ (go - ing gets tough) (when the go - ing gets rough,___ oh.___ (Go-

Verse 3:
I'm gonna buy me a one-way ticket
Nothing's gonna hold me back
Your love's like a soul train coming
And I feel it coming down the track.

(Darling) I'll climb any mountain *etc.*

you needed me

You need-ed me

1. I cried a tear you wiped it dry I was con-fused,

(Verse 2 see block lyric)

you cleared my mind. I sold my soul, you bought it back

D.𝄌. al Coda

fin - 'lly found— some-one— who real - ly cares._____ (You need-ed me) 2. You held— my hand

Coda

- ed me.____ You need - ed me.____ You need - ed me.____ Oh yes you need-

rit.

- ed me.____ You need-ed me._____

Verse 2:
You held my hand
When it was cold
When I was lost
You took me home
You gave me hope
When I was at the end
And turned my lies
Back into truth again
You even called me friend.

You gave me strength
To stand alone again *etc.*

when you say nothing at all

words & music by paul overstreet & don schlitz.

you can light up the dark.___

Try as I may I can nev - er ex - plain___ what I hear___ when you don't___

say a thing.___ The

smile on your face lets me know___ that you need___ me. There's a

smile on your face   lets me know— that you need— me. There's a   truth in your eyes   say-ing you'll

——— nev - er leave——— me.   The   touch   of   your   hand   say's you'll   catch—

me where-ev-er I fall.

You say it best when you say no-thing at all.

(You say it best when you say no-thing at all.) (You say it best when you say

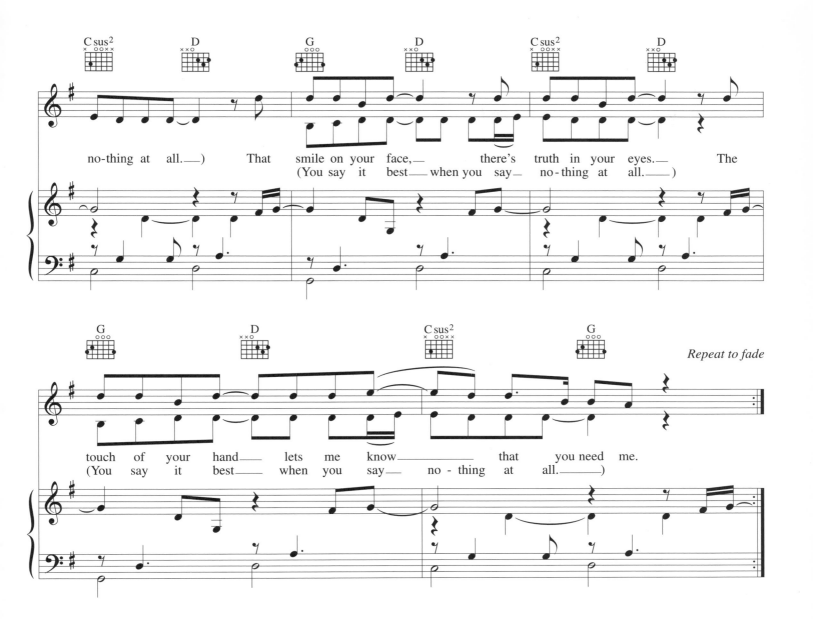

Verse 2:
All day long I can hear people talking out loud
But when you hold me you drown out the crowd
Try as they may they can never defy
What's been said between your heart and mine.

The smile on your face *etc.*

all the time in the world

words & music by dave robbins, van stephenson & desmond child.

Verse 2:
I know it's hard to let me love you
When our trust is on the line
I know it takes a lot of courage
When your faith is hard to find
But I've never tried to hurt you
I fight heaven and earth to protect you
So take your time and feel me near you
There's nothing to fear when I'm with you.

Cos I've got all the time in the world *etc.*

i'll never not need you

words & music by diane warren. © copyright 1998 realsongs, usa. emi music publishing limited, 127 charing cross road, london wc2. all rights reserved. international copyright secured.

Verse 2:
I don't want no-one else's kisses
I'll never hunger for another's touch
Oh there'll be no-one else this heart will ever love.
You can be sure I am yours forever
Cos you're my world baby, world baby.

I'll never not want you *etc.*